Disney PRINCESS

Snow White
and the Seven Dwarfs

Learning Numbers

Phidal

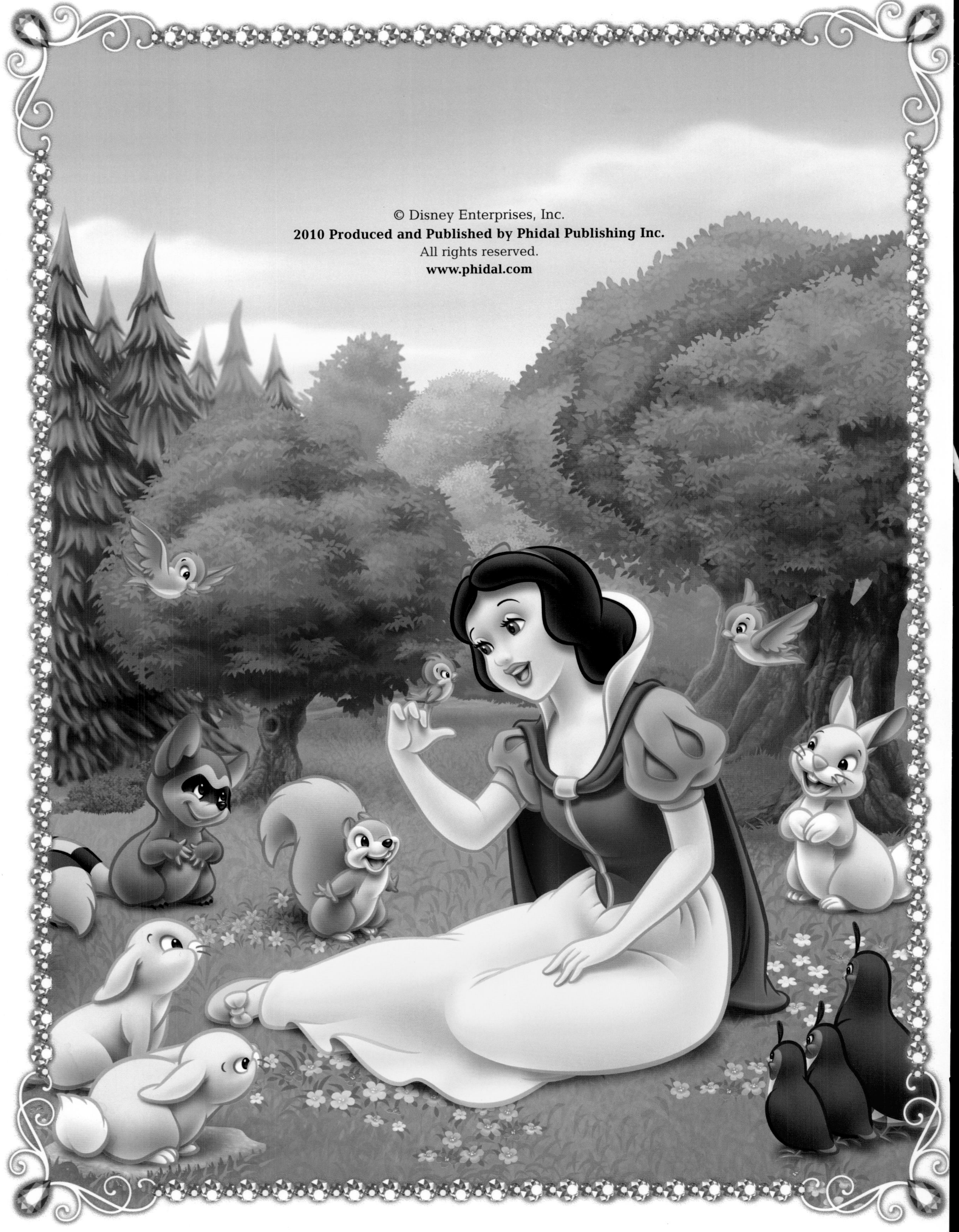

Count from 1 to 10

Can you find the stickers that match these numbers?

What Comes Next?

Which rabbit would you pick to complete the series?

Do you think that the missing number will be yellow or red?

121212

Can you find the missing animals?

Which numbers are missing in this series?

1234567

Counting for fun

Fill in the chart by adding the correct number of objects.

Now that you've finished the chart, how many mirrors are there?

How many golden crowns can you count?

How many red apples are there?

Counting at the Cottage

Snow White is looking for the Seven Dwarfs.
Can you count the objects and animals that surround her?

1 Fawn

2 Mushrooms

3 Deer

4 Raccoons

5 Nests

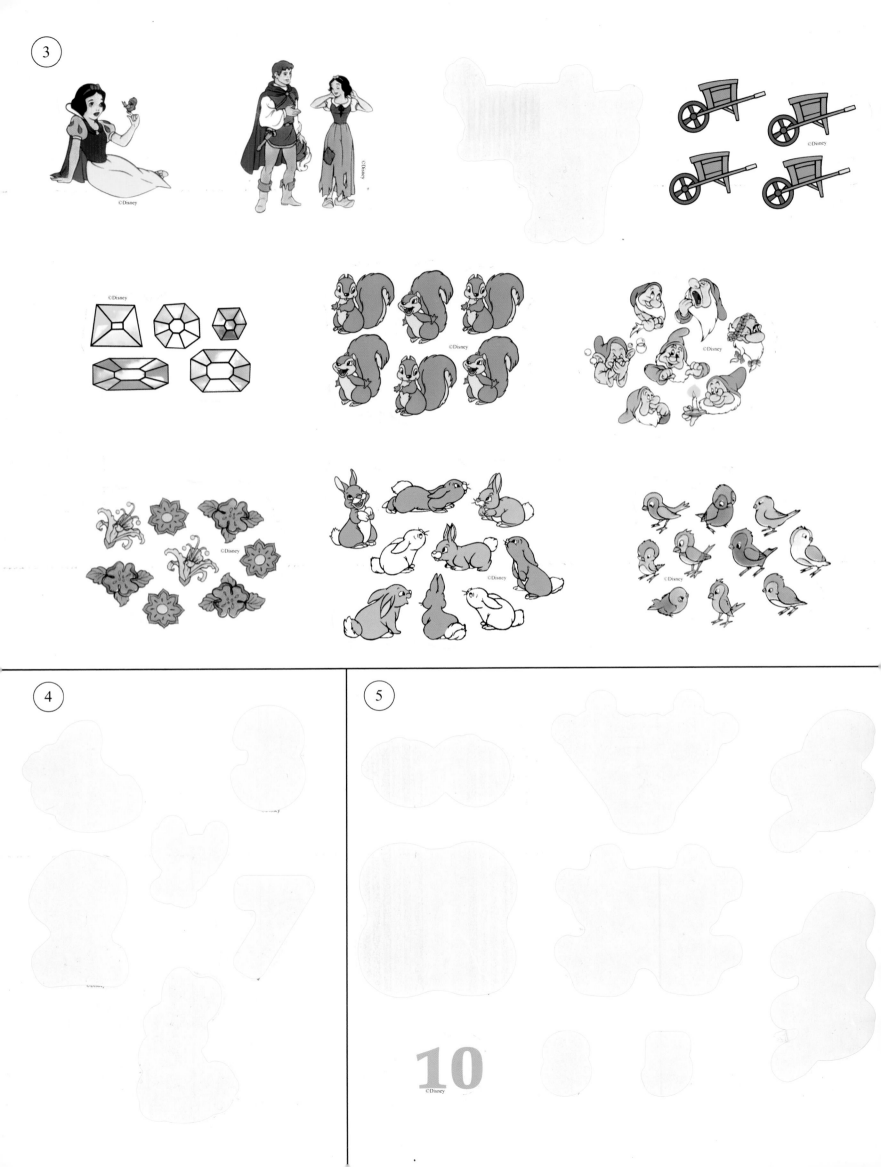

3

4

5

10

Window panes **6**

Squirrels **7**

Flowers **8**

Birds **9**

Rabbits **10**

Time to Add

Help Snow White solve this problem.

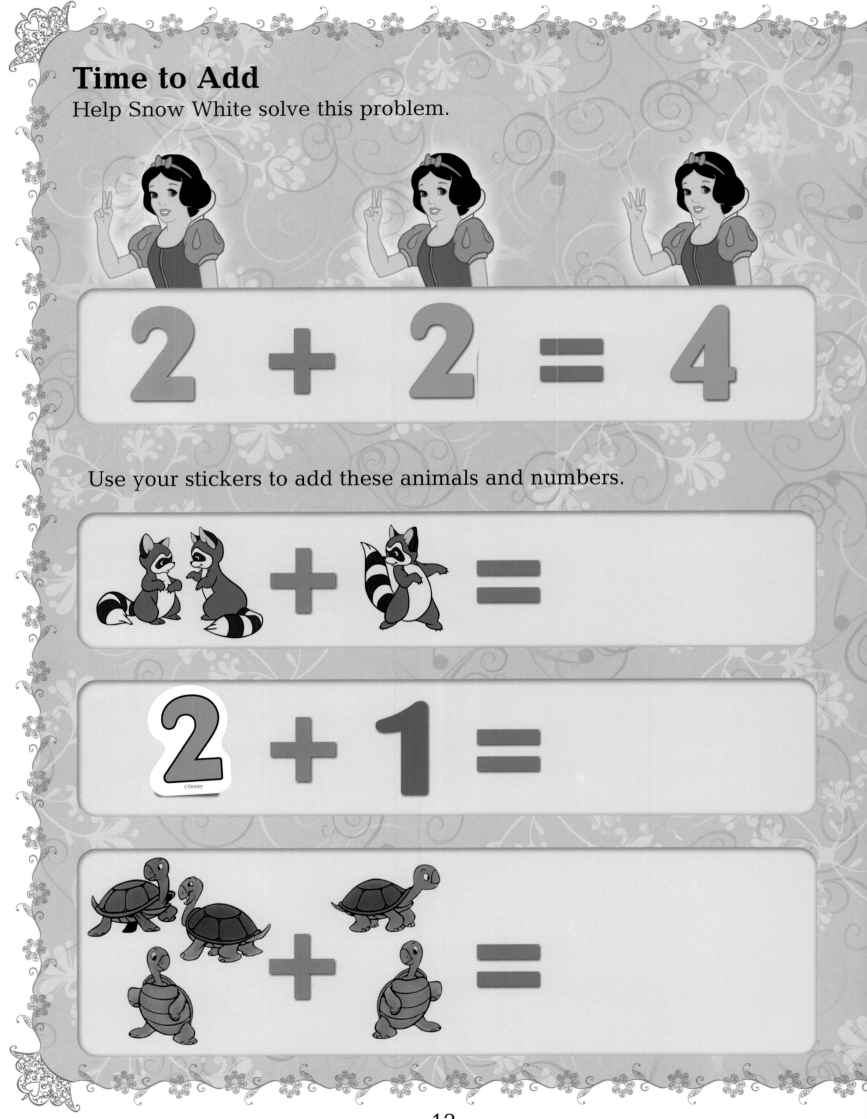

$$2 + 2 = 4$$

Use your stickers to add these animals and numbers.

$$2 + 1 =$$

+ **=**

$2 + 5 =$

+ **=**

4
$+1$
$= 5$

4
$+4$
$=$

7
$+3$
$=$

Time to Subtract

Help Snow White solve this problem.

$$3 - 2 = 1$$

Use your stickers to solve these subtraction problems.

$$7 - 2 =$$

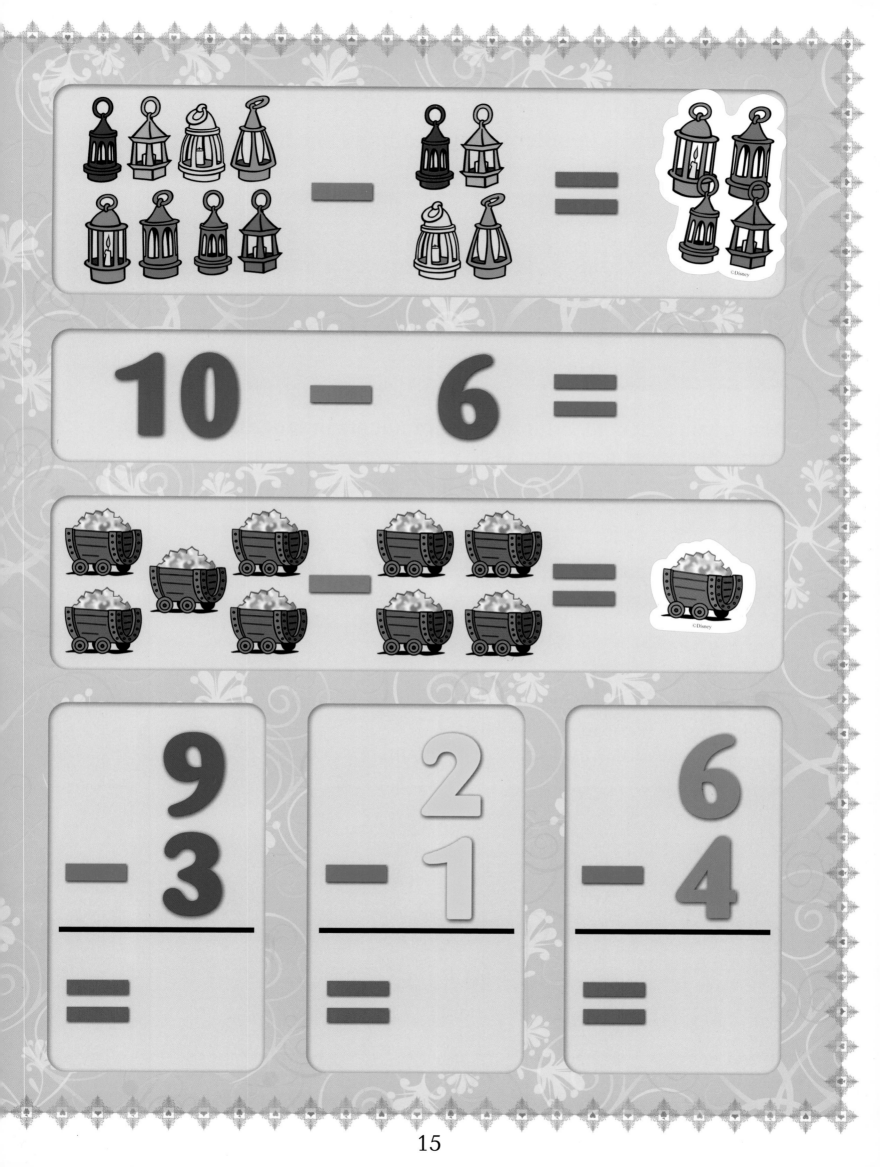

$$10 - 6 =$$

$$\begin{array}{r} 9 \\ -\ 3 \\ \hline \end{array}$$

$$\begin{array}{r} 2 \\ -\ 1 \\ \hline \end{array}$$

$$\begin{array}{r} 6 \\ -\ 4 \\ \hline \end{array}$$

All in Order

Put these animals in order starting with the one that has the least number of legs.

Using your stickers, arrange these numbers in order from 1 to 10, from the lowest to the highest.

1 3 5 6 7 8 10

The Seven Dwarfs are not very tidy. Help Snow White sort the dishes, going from the biggest pile to the smallest.

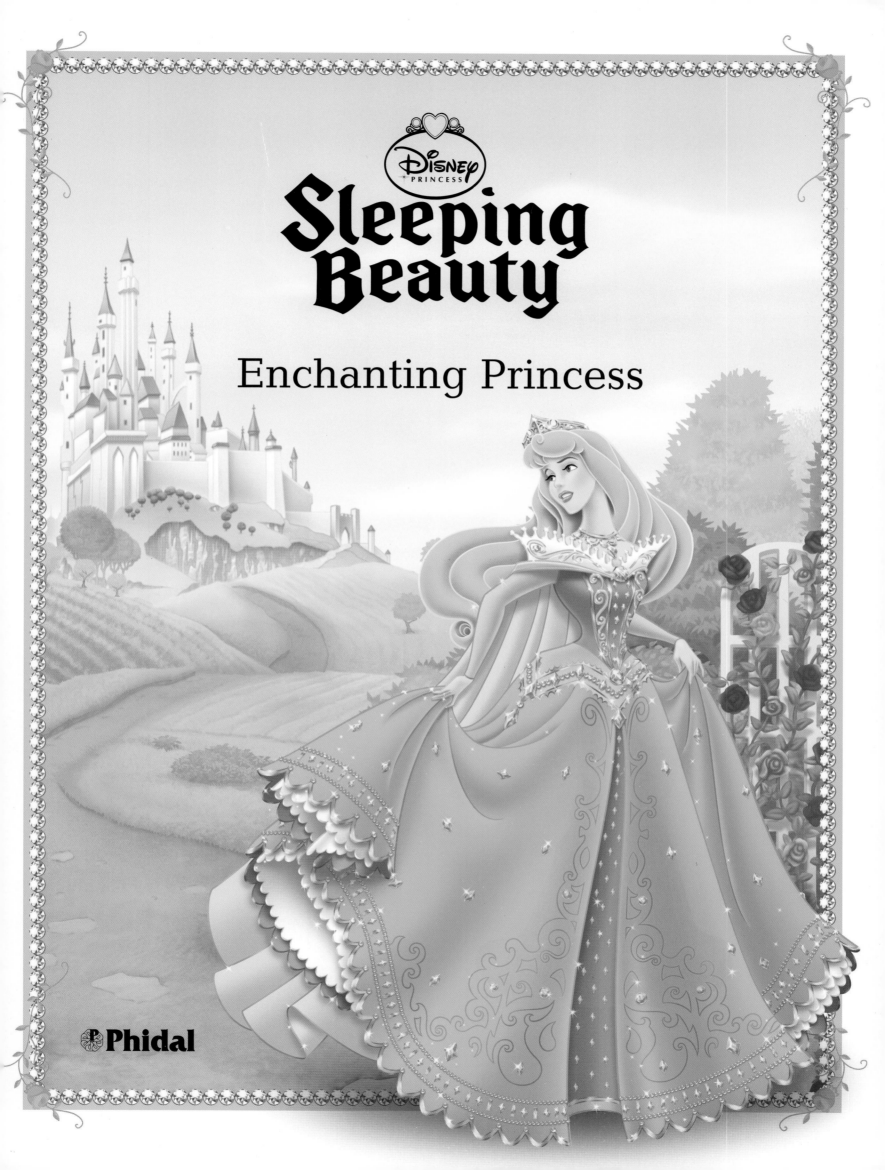

Sleeping Beauty

Enchanting Princess

Phidal

2010 Produced and Published by Phidal Publishing Inc.

www.phidal.com

Matching Magic

The Good Fairies wave their wands. Place each sticker with its matching color.

Green

Orange

Blue

3

What's Missing?

Look at the first scene, and then complete the same scene below with your stickers.

Follow the Trail

Match each person with their missing object or companion.

The Enchanted Forest

Aurora meets her prince in the forest. Use your stickers to decorate the scene.

6 11

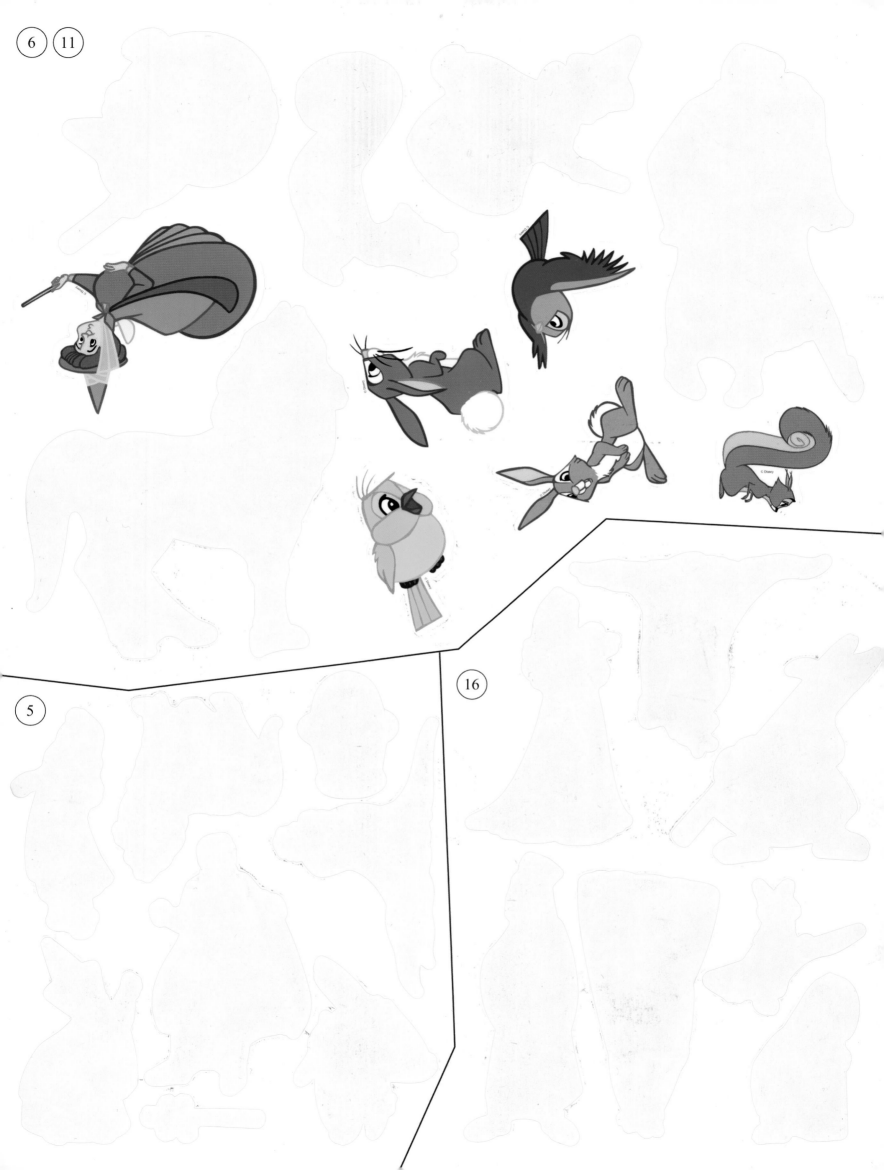

5

16

Cottage Celebration

Aurora admires her lovely cake! Use your stickers to count the objects below.

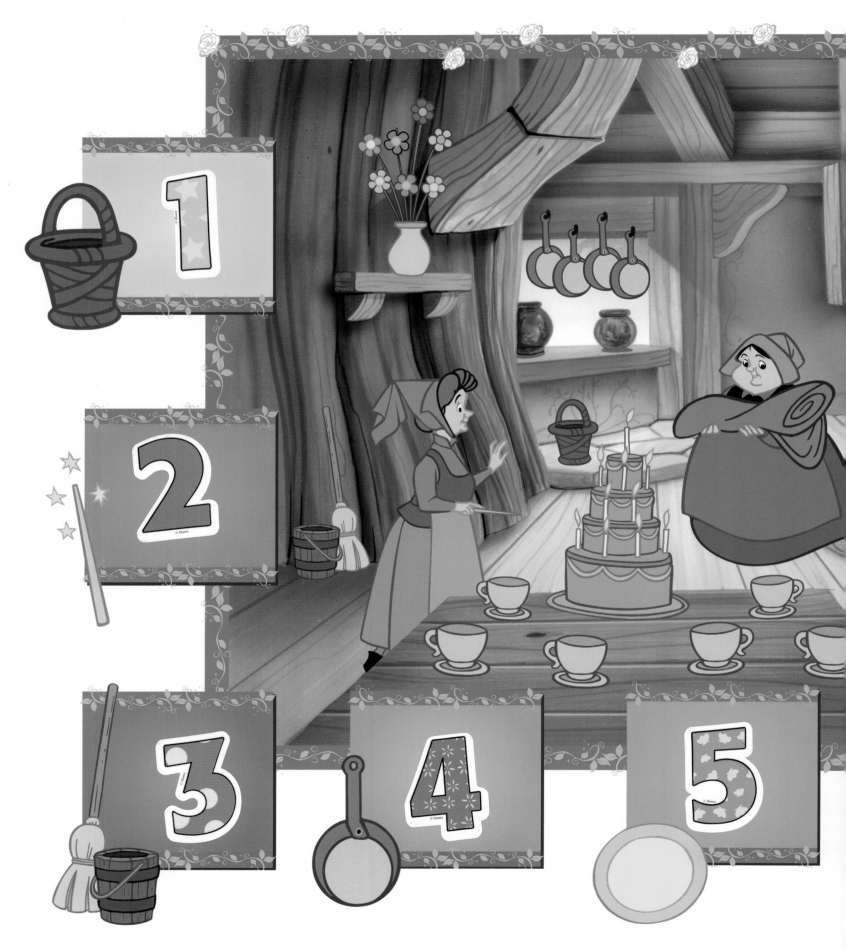

All in Order

Complete each series with the help of your stickers.

Facing front and facing back

Facing right and facing left

From the most to the least

Who's in the Castle?

Use your stickers to fill in the shadows.

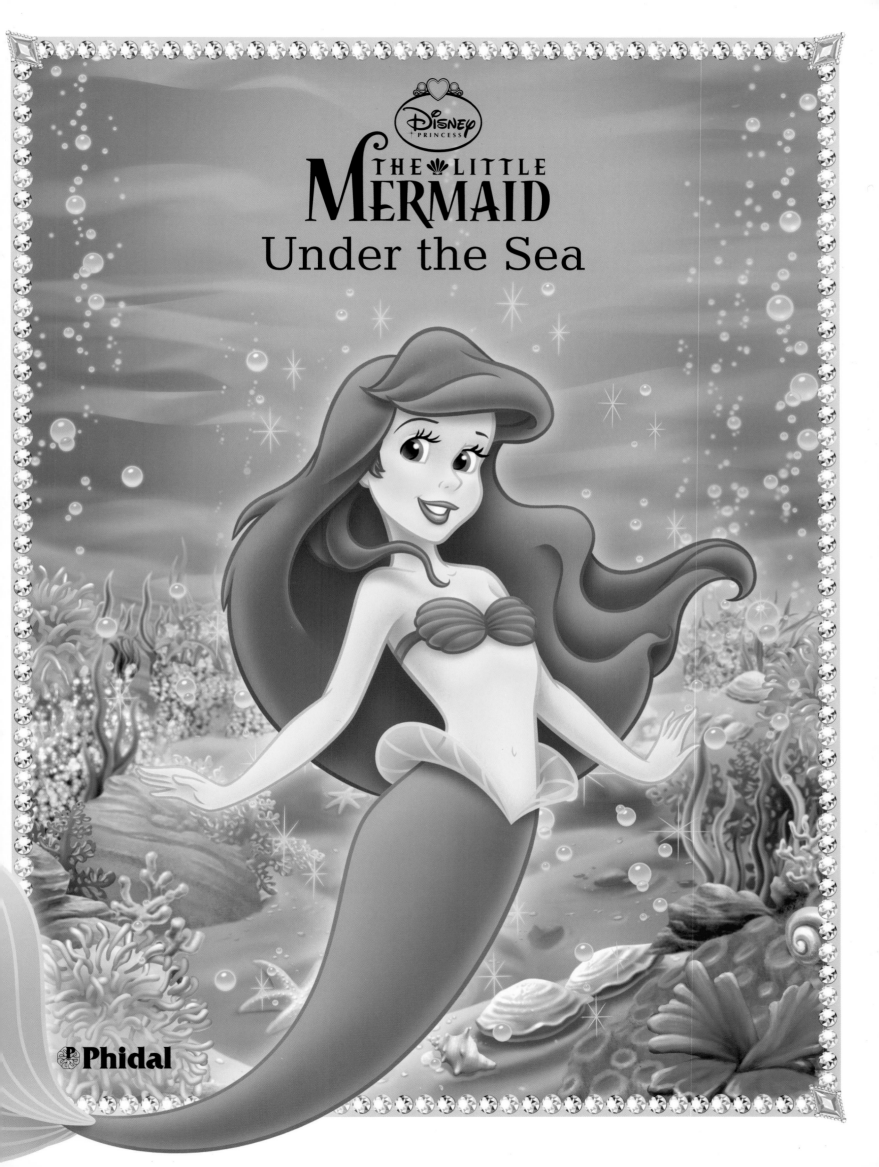

On Dry Land
Who lives on land above the water?

Under the Sea
Who lives below the sea's surface?

Marine Life

Complete the food chain with the help of your stickers.

Seabirds

Seagull

Shark

Mackerels

Orca

Litt

Seabream

Big predators

Medium siz

Sea Lion

Dolphin

Octopus

Sea mammals

Squid

Mollusks

Coral

Herrings

Plankton

...sh

Cod

...sh

Swordfish

Tuna

Big fish

Shellfish

Crayfish

Seaweed

Fun Under the Sea!

The ocean is full of wonders! Decorate the scene with your stickers.

Sea Shapes

Place the same shapes together in rows with the help of your stickers.

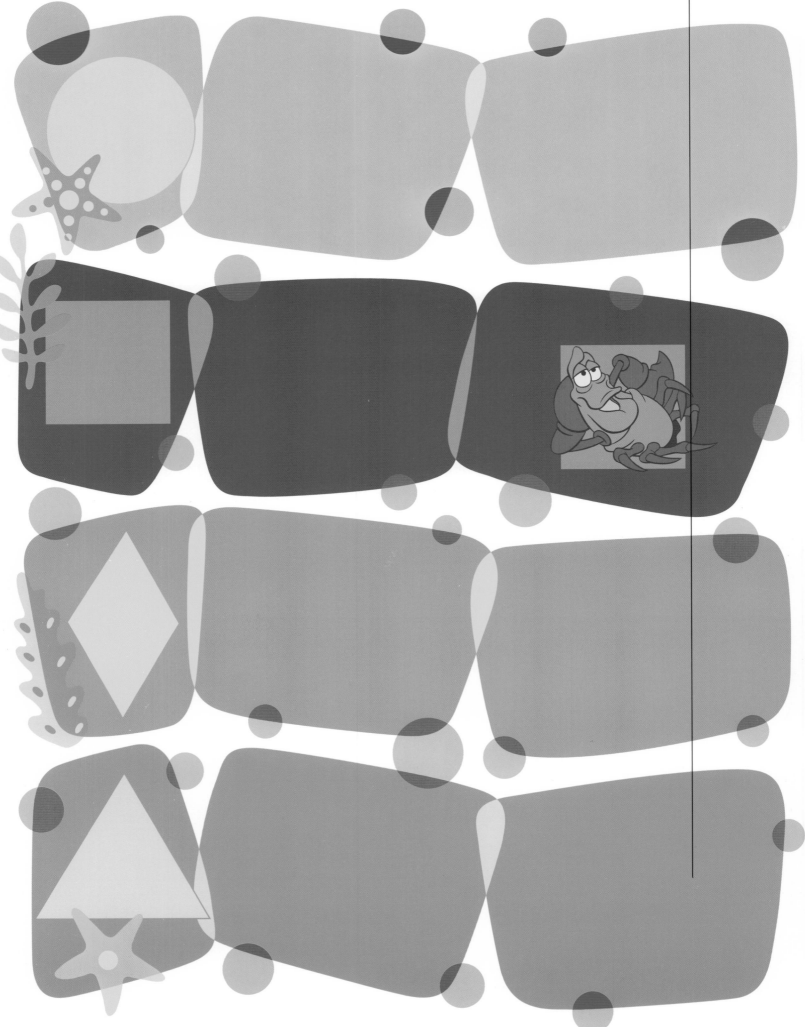

Ariel's Cave

Help Ariel place the objects . . .

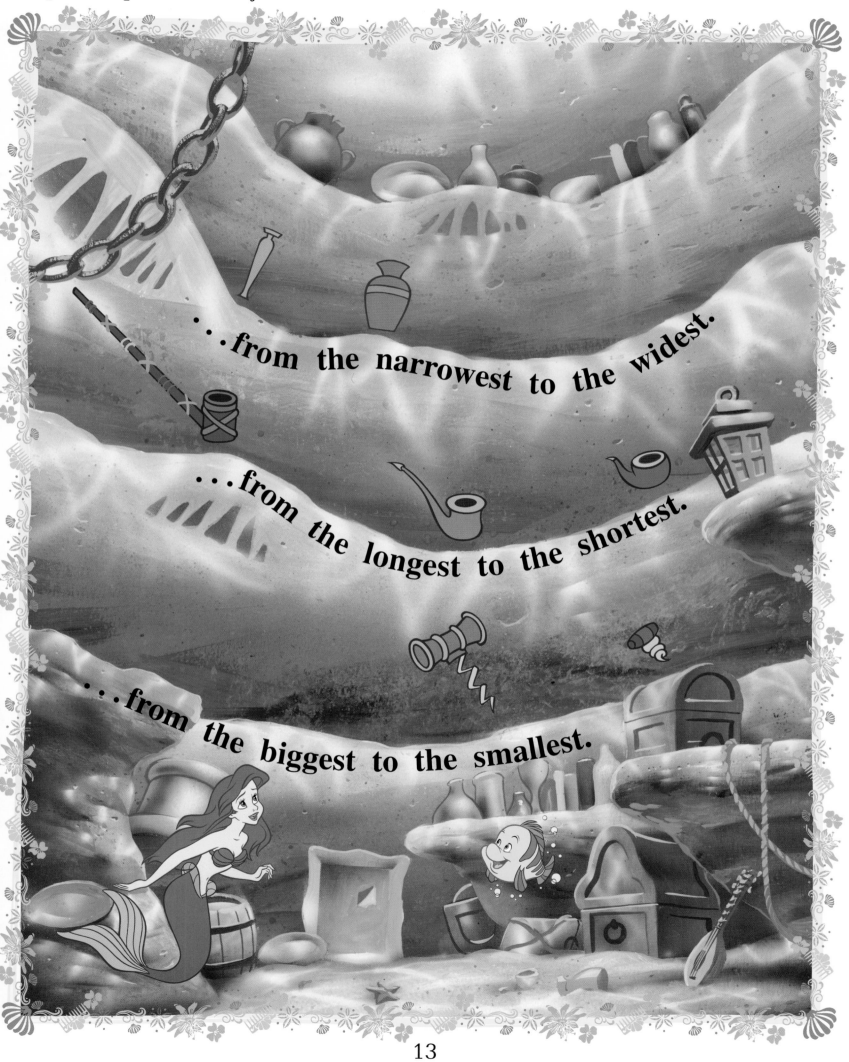

. . .from the narrowest to the widest.

. . .from the longest to the shortest.

. . .from the biggest to the smallest.

Counting in the Ocean
Group together and count these sea things.

How many fish?

5

How much coral?

How many seashells?

The Evil Ursula

Ursula and her eels are up to no good! Place your stickers over the shadows.

From the Sea

Use your stickers to discover these useful products from the sea.

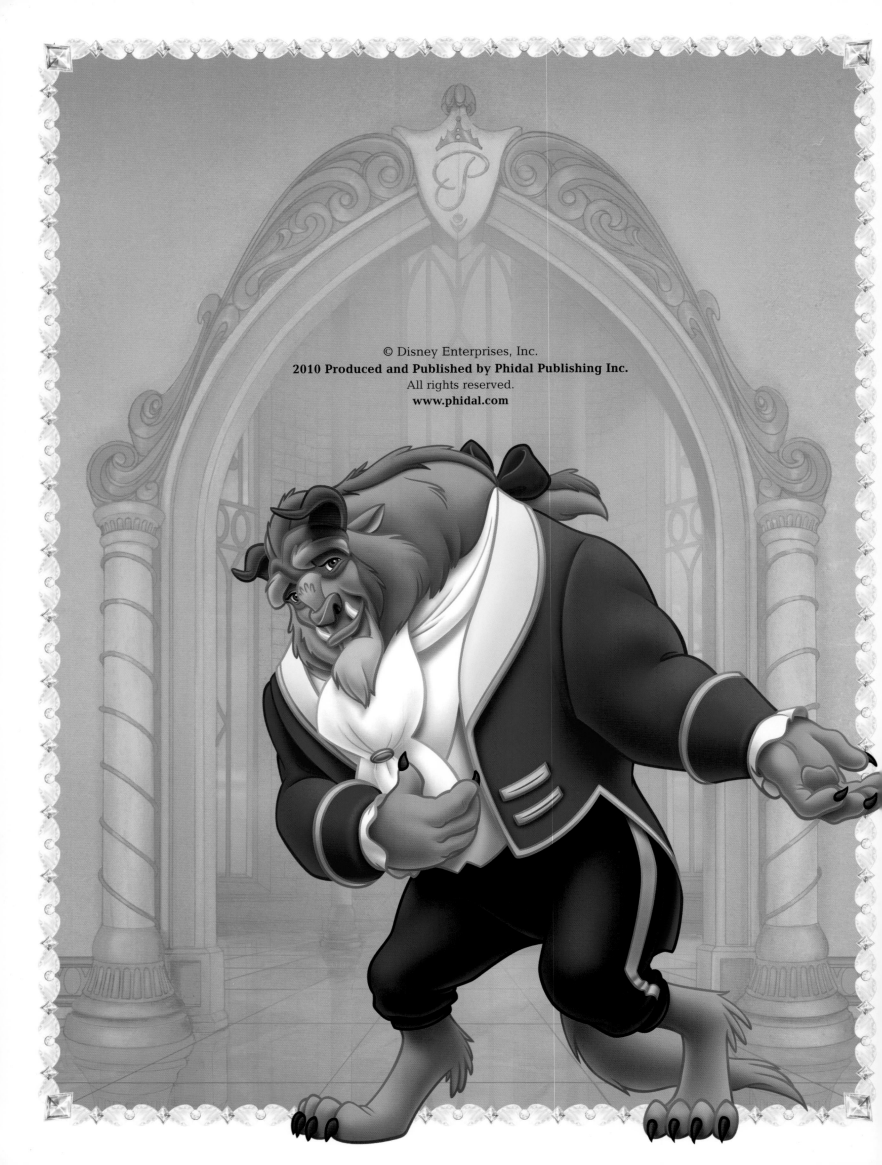

Who Lives in the Castle?

Discover these friendly characters by placing your stickers on the shadows they match.

Sort It Out

Can you place the objects and animals in the right area of the castle?

Kitchen

Bedroom

Living Room

Yard

A Magical Night

The castle friends are dancing in the ballroom. Decorate the scene with your stickers.

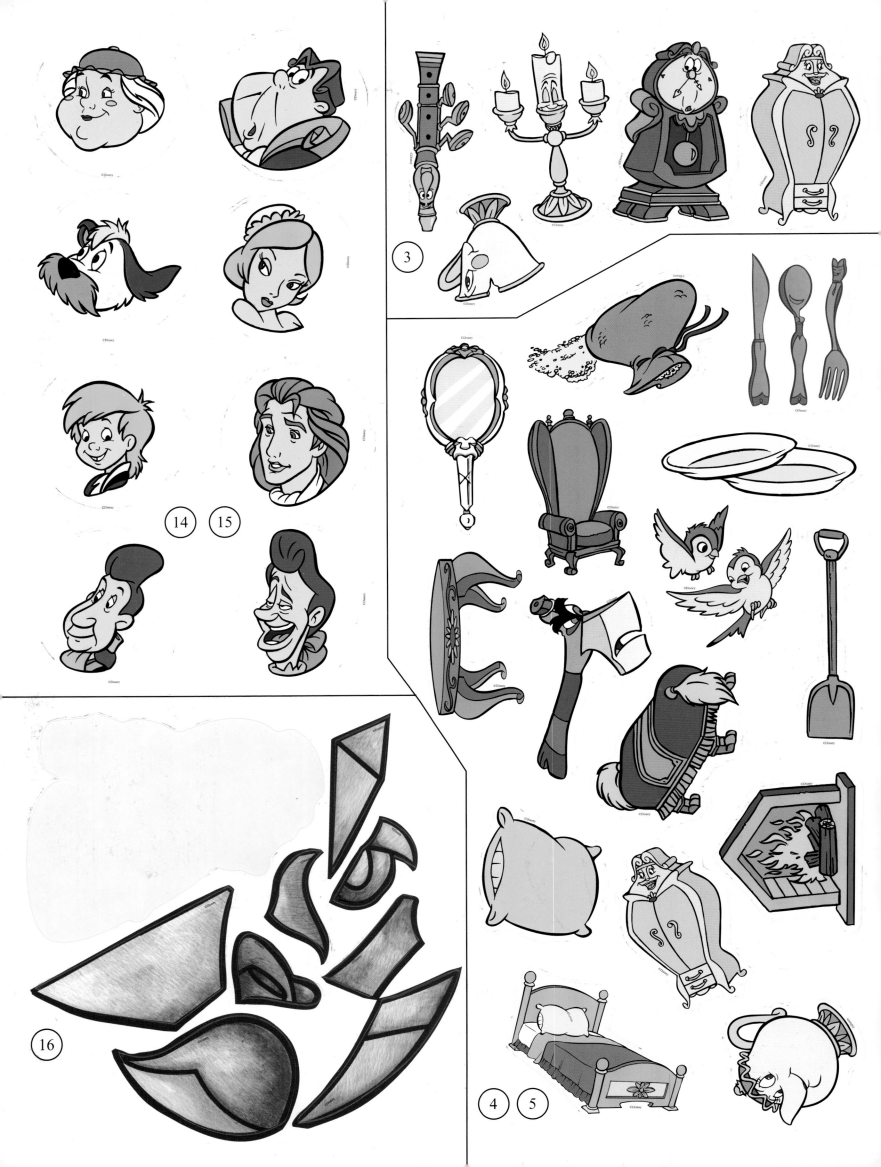

Matching Opposites

Can you find the opposite of each image with your stickers?

brave

afraid

boy

girl

one

many

good

evil

full

fresh

wilting

empty

calm

mad

big

small

up

down

The Power of the Rose

Will the Beast find true love before the last petal falls? Find out with your stickers.

THE PRINCESS AND THE FROG

A Dream Come True

City Folk and Bayou Buddies

With the help of your stickers, place each character in the right scene below.

The City

The Bayou

Who's on the Scene in New Orleans?
Do you know who all the characters are? Find out with your stickers.

Princess Tiana

Prince Naveen

Ray

Louis

Lawrence

4

Mama Odie

Dr. Facilier

Naveen & Tiana
as frogs

Charlotte

Big Daddy

Bayou Boogie

The evening swamp is alive with music! Decorate the scene with your stickers.

3

4 5

6 11

Mystical Match-Up
Place the characters below with the right object or friend using your stickers.

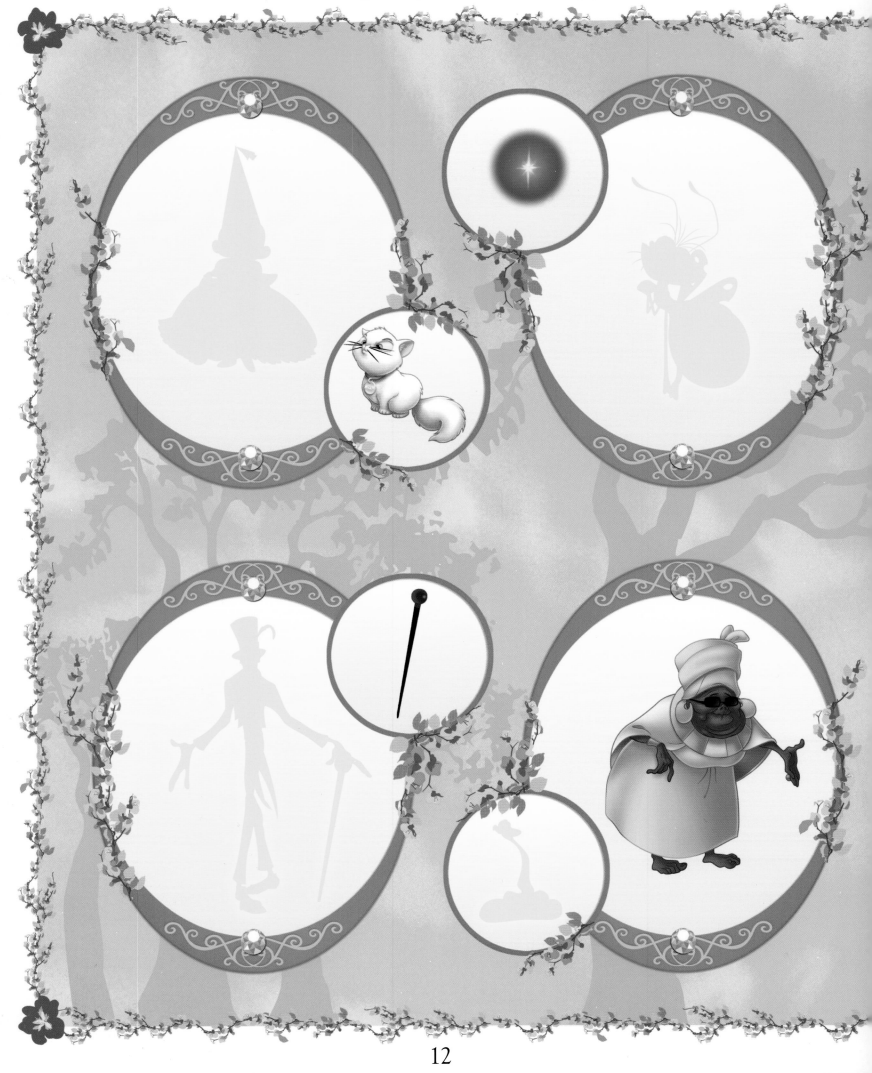

Southern Scenes

Who belongs in which picture? Place your stickers over the right shadows.

A Magical Moment

The bayou is a mystical place! Make the bottom scene look like the top one with your stickers.

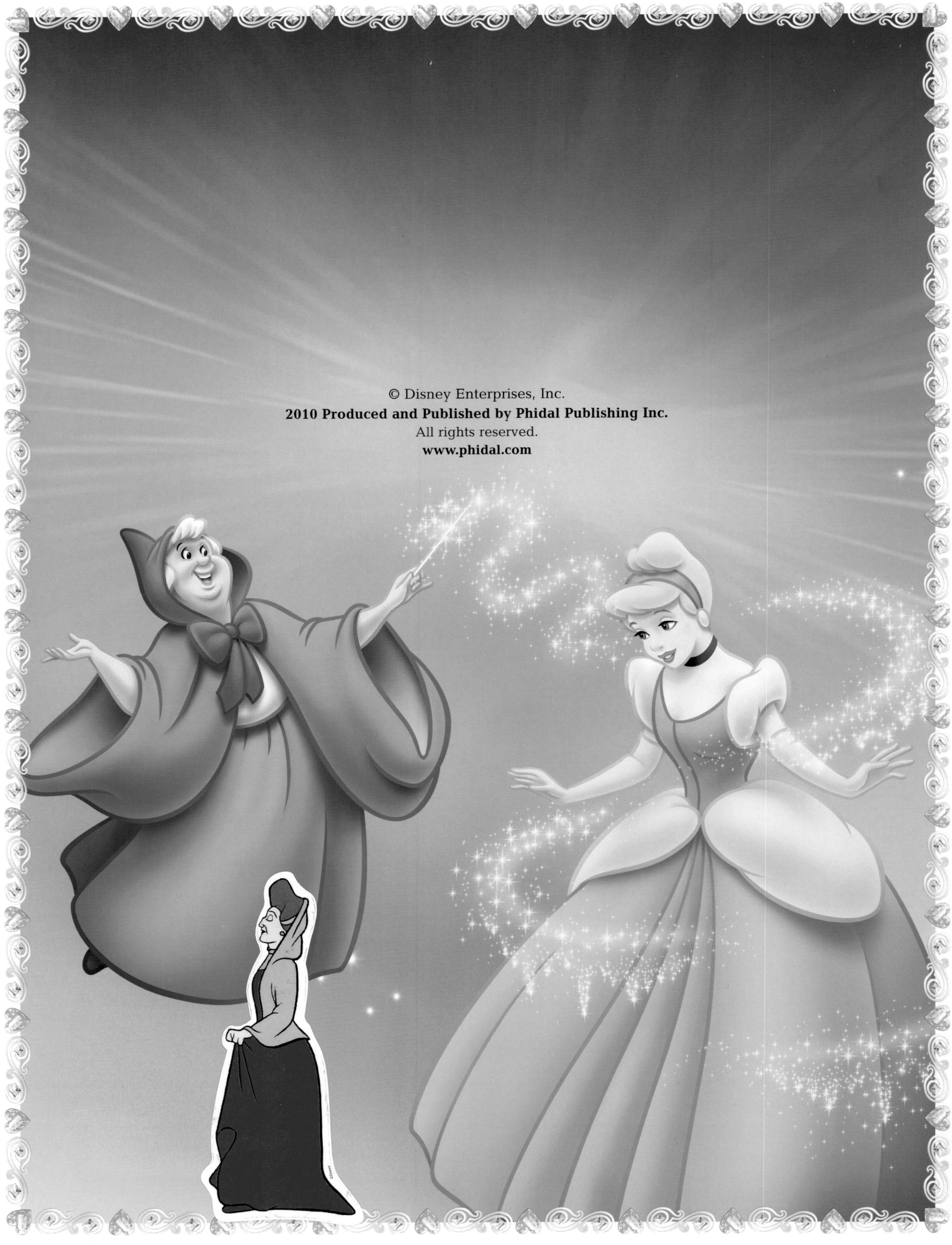

What a Mess!

Use your stickers to help Cinderella clean up in time for the ball!

Work and Play

Can you count the characters and objects in the scene using your stickers?

A Magical Evening

The palace ball is a dazzling event! Use your stickers to decorate the scene.

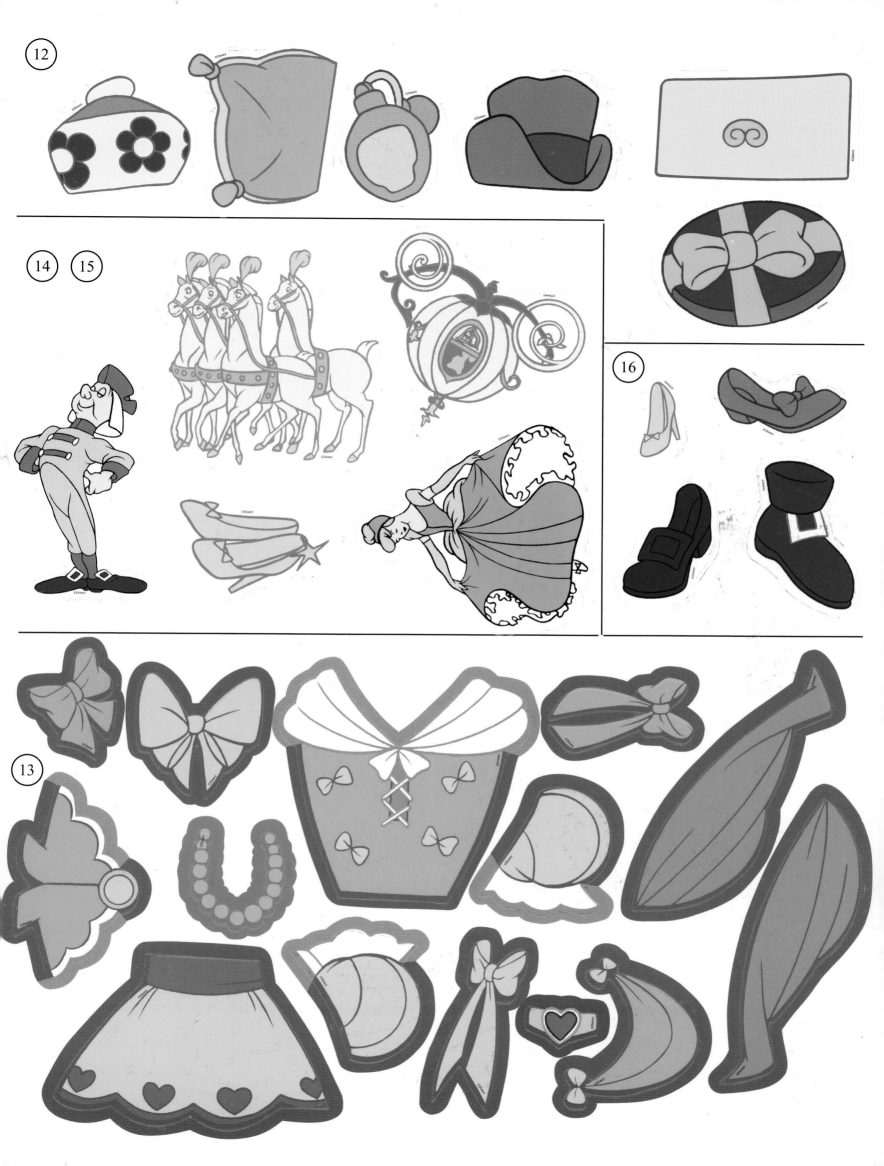

Hide-and-Seek

Help the mice hide from Lucifer the wicked cat.

A Gown for the Ball

Can you create a beautiful gown for Cinderella?

Magical Makeovers

Use your stickers to transform these characters and objects in time for the ball.

If the Shoe Fits

Who fits the glass slipper? Match these characters with their missing shoe.